G000254287

THE ROSLAND BOOK OF GOLD

ROSLAND CAPITAL LIMITED

ISBN: 978-0-9934523-0-7

Published by Rosland Capital Limited

First published July 2014. This edition printed in July 2017.

THE ROSLAND GUIDE TO

GOLD

Your guide to becoming an owner of real Gold

CALL ROSLAND ON 0800 902 0000

rosland.co.uk

'One of the world's rarest and most sought after collector coins, the 1933 Double Eagle, was sold at Sotheby's in New York in 2002 for the record sum of $7.59 million.

The coin led an eventful life – escaping a big gold meltdown in the US, falling into the hands of an Egyptian King and then being discovered by undercover secret service agents in New York.'

OWNING REAL GOLD HAS NEVER BEEN EASIER:
the How, the Why and the Who to Talk To.

Since 2008, Rosland has been in the business of helping people get their hands on precious gold coins. To do so, we work closely with each customer to help them decide on the right choice of coins for them. There are so many to choose from...

... coins that originate from every corner of the globe. They all have their individual beauty and many have amazing stories to tell: how they were used, which artisans crafted them and of course, who owned them. And what better place to start collecting real gold coins than with Rosland?

We've helped thousands of people to realise their dream of owning something of real and lasting beauty.

Every gold coin represents a fantastically rich nugget of history – a place in time and culture that'll never be repeated. Each one is also the summation of thousands of years of technical development... using techniques of refining, modelling and finishing that have been honed and perfected over many generations of craftsmen. With help from Rosland, you can soon enjoy these marvels in your own home.

Rosland, one of the leading Gold Specialists in the US, now arrives in the city of London

Rosland Capital was founded in 2008 by a 20-year veteran of the precious metals industry. The US company is based in Los Angeles, California, though its customers come from every state. The gold and silver it offers comes from sources around the world, including the US Mint and the Royal Mint.

In early 2014 Rosland opened an office in London, offering a wide range of coins and other artefacts as well.

Rosland is proud to feature well-loved American actor William Devane in its TV advertising campaign. Mr Devane has worked with the US company for a number of years and is a keen supporter of purchasing gold and silver.

'At the end of 2011, it was estimated that all the gold ever mined totalled 171,000 metric tonnes. This can be represented by a cube with an edge length of about 20.28 metres.

At approximately $1,300 per troy ounce, 171,000 metric tonnes of gold would have a value of $7.1 trillion.'

IN THE BEGINNING, THERE WAS GOLD...

Gold was first smelted as long ago as 3600BC. Egyptian goldsmiths carried out the first melting or fusing of ores in order to separate the metals inside. They used blowpipes made from fire-resistant clay to heat the smelting furnace.

A thousand years later we find one of the earliest examples of gold jewellery in the ancient empire of Mesopotamia (modern-day Iraq). It's a stunning burial headdress of lapis and carnelian beads set within delicate gold pendants shaped like the leaves of the willow tree.

Most famously in modern times, the discovery of the tomb of Tutankhamun brought to light the extraordinary gold funeral mask - a triumph of gold craftsmanship exactly as it was last seen by its remarkable creator around 3,000 years ago.

Probably the first gold currency was created by King Croesus, who improved gold refining techniques, permitting him to mint the world's first standardised currency. Their uniform gold content allowed 'Croesids' to become universally recognised and traded with confidence.

Right here in England the world's first hallmarking system, scrutinising and guaranteeing the quality of precious metal was established at Goldsmith's Hall in London around the year 1300. And in fact, that is still where London's Assay Office is located today, some 700 years later.

It was 1848 when the California Gold Rush began. It all started when a certain John Marshall discovered gold flakes while building a sawmill near Sacramento, California. In the rush that followed, 40,000 diggers flocked from all over the world to try their luck. Just 40 years later a similar gold fever struck South Africa after an Australian miner named George Harrison found gold ore on a farm near Johannesburg. South Africa went on to become the source of around 40 per cent of the world's gold.

In 610BC, the ancient Lydians of Asia Minor minted the first Gold coins.

According to the Greek historian, Herodotus, the Lydians were the first people to use gold and silver coins. From the evidence of coin hoards and archaeological research, it is now believed that the earliest coins of Lydia were produced in the late 7th century BC.

By 630BC they had developed into the lion's head emblem of the Mermnad dynasty of Lydia, of which King Croesus - whose wealth was proverbial in the ancient world - was the fifth and final ruler. This emblem was applied to the obverse or 'heads' side, by placing the lump of metal (called a blank or flan) on an anvil whose top had been engraved with the design. The blank was heated until it was soft then struck with a hammer until an image of the design was left impressed on the surface of the blank. The earliest coins were uni-face or one-sided, but gradually it became customary to include a simple geometric design that bit into the reverse or 'tails' side of the coin.

The credibility that these simple designs gave came to be regarded as a guarantee of their value. The value was still linked to the weight and precious metal used, but it was no longer necessary to weigh each coin separately at every transaction.

The first electrum coins were found on the river bed of the Pactolus in Asia Minor and may have been struck for King Ardys of Lydia, ancestor of Croesus. From there they spread to other parts of western Asia Minor, being adopted by the Greek coastal towns of Abydus, Chios, Miletus and Phocaea. These early coins had no inscriptions as they circulated only within their own territories, but their motifs were clues to their identity, such as the sphinx of Chios and the man-bull of Miletus. One of the earliest Greek coins showed the civic emblem of a stag and was inscribed: 'I am the sign of Phanes'. Soon, by the 6th century, production spread from Asia Minor to mainland Greece.

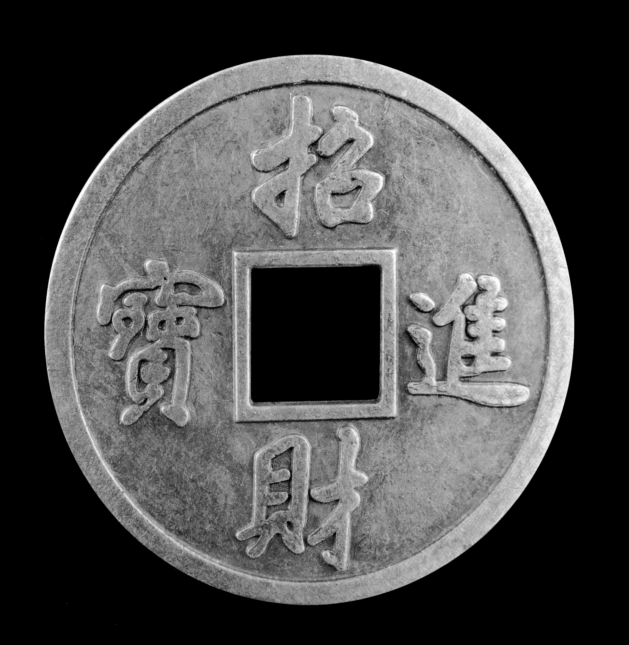

Gold coins from early China, the Roman Empire… and beyond.

The development of the earliest coinage was simultaneous in China and Asia Minor. The first Chinese coins were small pieces of bronze, cast into representations of the useful agricultural implements used in barter.

Small knives, spades, keys and other domestic articles, symbols of the earlier barter system, were invested with a notional value and had no utilitarian purpose. But they represented a real value and could be exchanged for goods or services accordingly.

By the 4th century BC, bronze circular discs with a hole in the centre were in circulation. Over several generations, these pieces evolved into the regular banliang (half ounce) coins minted by the Emperor Shi Huang-di, founder of the Qin dynasty, in 221BC and known as 'cash'. In 118BC the banliang were replaced by wuzhu (5 grain) coins by the Han emperor Wudi. These were used all over China, even after the empire was split into a number of smaller states in AD 220.

Meanwhile, and closer to home, developments were well underway in the Roman Empire. In fact, our connection with the Roman world can be seen in many of our units of currency and weight. The Latin word pondus, for example, has given us such words as 'ponder' (to weigh up), 'ponderous' (heavy) and 'pound', used both as a weight and a unit of currency.

Although an imperial mint to supply silver and gold coins was not established in Rome until 269BC, the Romans had been striking bronze coins locally for several decades prior to this. These bronze currencies began with the 'aes rude', whose name refers to the crudeness of unmarked lumps of metal, which had to be weighed out at each transaction.

More ancient coinage started appearing in many corners of the globe. At the fall of the Roman Empire in the west, their other outpost in the east in Byzantium (or Roman Constantinople) minted coins with the portrait of their ruler, Theodoric on one side and a figure of Rome on the other, with the caption 'Invicta Roma' (unconquered Rome).

Celtic peoples settled in the British Isles and developed their own distinctively celtic coinage in the late pre-Christian era, imitating the gold and silver coins with which they were most familiar – the gold staters of the Alexandrine Empire and its Hellenistic successors.

THE GOLD COINS FROM EUROPE:

the Kingdoms of the Middle Ages

With the collapse of Rome, the barbarian tribes of Europe were on the move, and from that great migration arose the ancient states of Europe… Normandy, the kingdom of the Franks, the Holy Roman Empire under Charlemagne, Burgundy, Lombardy and the principalities of Germany.

These states had to develop new coinage to replace the Roman silver currency in increasingly short supply. In 752, Pepin the Short, king of the Franks, issued a new silver coin, the denier, which quickly became a standard throughout the realm for the next six centuries. In 793, Charlemagne increased the weight of the denier by a third, and this led to the silver coins being adopted in the Balkans (Serbia uses the dinar to this day), in Italy, where it became the denaro, and the dinero of Spain.

It was also the model for the penny in England, which became the pfennig in the German states, the fenigow in Poland and the penni in Finland.

In the German states of the 12th and 13th century, extremely thin silver coins known as bracteates became popular – so thin they could only be struck on one side. In the 13th century, gold coins began to be re-introduced, heavily influenced by the Arab states that were pressing Europe. In southern Italy, the gold tari were inscribed with Arabic. The same influence can be seen in the silver ducat, so-called because it was first struck in the Duchy – the ducatus – of Apulia. The cavallino d'oro of Sicily and the 16th century zecchino of Venice were also notable coins of the ancient states of Europe.

From the dark ages to the 19th century, the emergence of modern coins and minting method

In the ruins of the Roman Empire, the small city states of Italy became the crossroads of civilisation and came under the influence of Lombards, Goths, Franks, Byzantines and Arabs too. Pope Adrian I minted the first papal coins, which continue to this day.

The gold coins in the Empire were demonetised and in 752 Pepin the Short issued a new silver coin, the silver denier (based on the Roman denarius), which became the basic unit of currency.

In the ruins of the Roman Empire, the small city states of Italy became the crossroads of civilisation and came under the influence of Romans, Goths, Franks, Byzantines and Arabs too. Pope Adrian I minted the first papal coins, which continue to this day.

By the 12th century, the Italian city states were at the forefront of the commercial revolution and their prosperity was reflected in the size and the quality of their coins, as well as the extent to which they were coveted and copied elsewhere. Venice, the greatest trading city of this period, introduced the zecchino or sequin, while its rival, Florence, produced a large silver coin depicting a lily. The coin, called a fiorino or florin, eventually passed into the currency of many countries, surviving until 2002 in the Netherlands (where the written symbol for a gulden was 'fl').

Up to this point, the production of coinage was very much an artisanal process. Each coin was a hand-crafted work of art.

However, the advent of steam power in the 18th century totally transformed the way coins were made. Previously, the maximum output using horsepower was around 40 coins per minute: using steam presses doubled that number immediately. This compares to today's high-speed electric presses that can make over 700 coins a minute. Matthew Boulton and James Watt invented milling and blank-cutting machinery powered by steam. First installed in 1786 at their Soho Mint in Birmingham, it was used to strike coins for the East India Company and many British trade tokens. In 1809 the firm began to supply the Royal Mint with steam powered machinery, which was then first used in the 'Great Recoinage' of 1816-17.

New Royal Mint
T.H. Shepherd 1830

Boulton also started negotiations with the US Mint in 1799, but it was not until 1816 that steam powered machinery was installed at the Philadelphia Mint.

ROSLAND'S
5 SIMPLE STEPS
TO BUYING GOLD

Call Rosland on
0800 902 0000
to talk to one of our
Gold Specialists,
without pressure or fuss

Rosland's Dealing Centre in London is staffed by knowledgeable, friendly professionals… real people, here in the UK, not in some far-away call centre. They're more than happy to talk about gold coins, the prices, what to look for – in fact, anything to do with the fascinating world of building your own collection of gold and other precious metals coins. There's no pressure whatsoever.

A personalised
portfolio option

If you wish, your Gold Specialist can help you create a personalised portfolio tailored to your financial position. Many collectors start with just a few coins and then build their collection over time. Your Gold Specialist can help you create the right mix of older coins, newly-minted coins, graded coins and perhaps something from our remarkable SS Republic hoard brought up from the bottom of the sea! And not just gold, either… there are silver and platinum options you can discuss.

A chance to reflect and discuss

Collecting coins is a very personal choice. Your Gold Specialist is more than happy to discuss fully the options open to you. You are never, ever, asked to make a decision 'on the spot'. That's not the Rosland way. Once you've discussed your ideas, then you're left to discuss it with your family and friends. Think it over. Call your Gold Specialist back any time (you'll always know who you're talking to, by name) if there are any questions at all.

Place your order on the phone

Buying your coins from Rosland couldn't be easier. Your Gold Specialist will confirm your order on a recorded telephone line, and then an account will be created for you. You will be sent Rosland's customer agreement for your perusal and signature. You are then a client of Rosland and your order can be processed. Your Gold Specialist will then discuss your preferred settlement method. We are happy to accept bank transfers, credit or debit cards, or cheques.

Shipped direct to you (or your nominated storage option) within 12 days

Your coins will then be ready to be shipped. You will be notified in advance of your delivery date. Alternatively, if you choose one of the many secure storage options you will be notified when the delivery has taken place.

A bank vault, a safe at home, private storage facilities… we can help you choose the right storage option for you.

THE GOLD COINS OF THE UNITED KINGDOM

The three kingdoms of the British Isles maintained separate identities for hundreds of years and each struck their own coins before they were united. England and Scotland had distinctive coins until the Act of Union in 1707, while Ireland ceased to mint its own coinage when the United Kingdom was formed by the Act of Union of 1801.

Celtic, tribal and Roman coins were used in Britain from the 2nd century BC until the withdrawal of the Roman legions in the early 5th century. These included gold Celtic ring money, Gallo-Belgic staters and coins of the major tribes in southern Britain. In succeeding generations, southern Britain was invaded by the Angles, Saxons and the Jutes, who established petty kingdoms in Northumbria, Kent, Mercia and East Anglia. Within these tribes, the earliest coins were small gold thrymsas and silver sceattas. But Offa of Mercia introduced the silver penny which remained the standard coin until the reign of Henry VII.

The Anglo-Saxon style of coinage was retained by the Normans and the Plantagenets. Edward I introduced the halfpenny and the farthing as well as the groat whilst Edward III struck half groats and the florin, which was England's first regular gold coin.

By the time of Henry VIII, coins in use included the Angel, Half-Angel, George Noble and the exotically-named Crown of the Double Rose, as well as the Sovereign. The minting of Sovereigns continued under Elizabeth I and James I.

Guineas came into use under Charles I, their name being derived from the gold's African source. Under George I, gold coins as small as the Quarter-Guinea were minted for a few years.

After the stresses of the Napoleonic Wars, when bank notes came into widespread use, the Royal Mint began a complete recoinage in 1816.

SOVEREIGN

The United Kingdom sovereign is a 22-carat gold coin, with a nominal value of one pound sterling. But in practice it is used as a bullion coin.

The English gold sovereign was last minted in 1604 and the name was revived with the Great Recoinage of 1816. Minting these new sovereigns began the following year; their gold content was fixed by the Coin Act of 1816 at 1320/5607 troy ounces, nearly equivalent to 113 grains. This weight has remained practically constant to the present day.

In the United Kingdom, sovereigns were minted from 1817 to 1917, in 1925, and from 1957. Australia, India, Canada and South Africa all occasionally minted the coins.

The initial reverse type for gold coins was the shield and crown motif, supplemented on the sovereign with a heraldic wreath. This was succeeded by a portrayal of Saint George killing a dragon, engraved by Benedetto Pistrucci. The same design is still in use, although other reverse designs have also been used during the reigns of King William IV, Queen Victoria, King George IV and Queen Elizabeth II.

BRITANNIA

The archetypical image of Britannia, seated with a shield, first appeared on Roman bronze coins of the 1st century AD, struck under Hadrian. But Britannia's first appearance on British coinage was on the farthing in 1672.

The figure of Britannia was said by Samuel Pepys to have been modelled on Frances Teresa Stuart, the future Duchess of Richmond, who was famous at the time for refusing to become the mistress of Charles II, despite the king's infatuation with her.

Britannia coins are bullion coins, issued by the Royal Mint in gold since 1987. Gold Britannias contain one troy ounce of gold and have a face value of £100. Gold Britannias are also issued in fractional sizes of one half, one quarter and one tenth of a troy ounce, with face values of £50, £25 and £10 respectively.

Since 2013, Britannia coins have been minted from 24-carat gold. In 2013, two additional sizes were introduced: a five ounce coin of face value £500 and a fractional size of one twentieth with a face value of £1.

THE GOLD COINS OF THE UNITED STATES

Although the Continental Congress of 1777 established a national mint, it was not until 1792 that the first one opened in Philadelphia. Until then the currency was a mess, with base metal subsidiary coins valued in pence or halfpence and silver based on the Spanish dollar. In common parlance, the Spanish 'Real' was known as a 'bit', and a quarter dollar was known as a 'two-bit coin', a term still used to signify 25 cents.

An interesting feature of United States coins is the inclusion of initials identifying the various branch mints, which were set up to refine and coin gold and silver mined locally. This practice continues to this day, although most US coins are now confined to base alloys.

The record for the second-highest price paid at auction for a single US coin is held by a 1933 Double Eagle, a $20 gold coin which sold for US$7.59m. Although hundreds of thousands of these coins were produced, no specimens were ever circulated and nearly all were melted down.

Precious metal coins currently minted by the U.S. include the Buffalo in 24-carat gold, and American Eagles in silver and in 22-carat gold. The gold Eagle features the image of Lady Liberty created by Augustus Saint-Gaudens, and used on the much-loved $20 face value coin shown to the right of this text.

The $2.5 and $5 "Indian Head" coins (1908-1929) designed by Augustus Saint-Gaudens are the only US coins with an 'incuse' design, meaning the image is sunk into the surface of the coin.

SAINT-GAUDENS

The Saint-Gaudens Double Eagle is a US$20 gold coin, produced from 1907 to 1933. It is named after its designer, the sculptor Augustus Saint-Gaudens, who designed the obverse and the reverse. Some consider it to be the most beautiful of all US gold coins.

Saint-Gaudens was proposed by President Theodore Roosevelt to beautify American coinage. Although he had an unhappy history with the US Mint and its chief engraver, Charles E Barber, he accepted the challenge. The work suffered many delays due to difficulties caused by the high relief of the design, but a modified version, which could be struck with a single blow, eventually went into production.

LIBERTY

This US$10 gold piece is often referred to as the Liberty Eagle. Versions of this coin were minted from 1838 to 1907. It depicts the crowned image of Lady Liberty on the front with the 13 stars representing the original 13 colonies. The reverse shows the traditional bald eagle image, with a shield on its breast, clasping three arrows in its left talon and an olive branch in its right. A classic image symbolising the power of Congress to bring both war and peace, respectively.

The eagle's head is turned to the right, signalling its preference for peace. It is interesting to note that the seal for the President of the United States was virtually the same, except the eagle faced the talon holding the arrows. In 1945, Harry S Truman changed it so that the seals were the same.

BUFFALO

The gold Buffalo is a 24-carat bullion coin, first offered for sale by the US Mint in 2006. The coin follows the greatly admired design of the Indian Head nickel and has gained its nickname from the American Bison on the reverse side of the design.

This was the first time ever that the US Government minted pure (.9999) 24-carat gold coins for the public. The coin has a legal tender value of US$50.

The obverse of the coin depicts a Native American, whom designer James Earle Fraser said he created as a mixture of the features of three chiefs from different American Indian tribes.

THE GOLD COINS OF CANADA

Early colonists, in what became Canada, originally used a mixture of English, French, Dutch and Spanish coins. Later on, coins were imported from England for its Canadian colony or from France, struck in Paris specifically for use in 'New France'. So it wasn't until the Canadian Mint was founded in 1908 that the country had its own production facility.

The Canadian Mint didn't start to produce bullion coins branded with the national emblem – a Maple Leaf – on the reverse until 1979. Since then Canada has become one of the world's leading producers of precious metals and the fineness of the gold used to strike the gold Maple Leaf has increased from .999 to .9999.

Using such pure gold means that the coins are actually quite soft and can easily become defaced by handling marks.

MAPLE LEAF

The official bullion coin of Canada, the Maple Leaf is one of the purest gold regular-issue coins produced, with a gold content of .9999 or even, in some special issues, .99999. That means it contains virtually no base metals at all, only gold from mines in Canada.

The coins are available in a number of denominations and are legal tender in Canada for their face values of $1, $5, $10, $20 and $50.

On May 3rd 2007 the Royal Canadian Mint unveiled a Gold Maple Leaf coin with a face value of $1 million, though the gold content of the coin was actually worth over $2 million at the time.

THE COINS
OF AUSTRALIA

The coins of Australia offer a wonderful window into the country's history and its unique fauna, while creating many interesting avenues for collectors.

Until the early 1850's the Australian colonies relied mainly on coinage from the mother country, but the gold rushes of 1851 changed the story. A mint was opened in Adelaide in 1852, so the metals found didn't have to be taken to London for minting. A mint in Sydney followed in 1853, which became a branch of the Royal Mint in 1870 and remained in production until 1926. Mints were also established in Melbourne, in 1872, and Perth, in 1899, and both of these are still active today.

The Perth Mint, wholly owned by the Government of Western Australia, is now recognised as the source of some of the most attractive, high quality bullion coins in the world. They're known for featuring the animals that are world-wide symbols of Australia.

Those animals got a very early start. The kangaroo appeared in 1823 on the first tradesman's token manufactured in Australia. The kangaroo was then often paired with the emu to create a pair of Australian 'heraldic supporters', in place of the lion and unicorn. They entered official usage in 1910 on a number of silver coins, and the kangaroo reappeared in 1938 as part of a series that also featured ears of wheat and a merino ram.

Over the years since then, animals shown on Australian coins have included the Platypus, Echidna, Frill-necked Lizard, Feather-tailed Glider, Palm cockatoos, Great White sharks, and the Kookaburra, which has long been a fixture on Australian silver bullion.

The Koala is a relatively recent arrival in Australian coin designs, but it adorned platinum bullion coins before migrating to silver, where it can be found on coins from 10 cents to 30 dollars, containing from 0.0992 oz. silver to 31.9118 oz., or 1 kilo, like the coin shown opposite.

The Gold Kangaroo, meanwhile, grew out of the Australian Nugget series, and it has appeared with gold content from 0.051 oz. (A$5) to 31.915 oz. (A$10,000). The coins were initially .999 gold, but they are now .9999, and they're widely admired for their rich color.

What makes the Kookaburra, the Koala and the Kangaroo coins even more interesting is that each year the animals are shown in different poses, from different angles, sometimes single, sometimes multiple, so that each year's design creates a new subject to collect.

Austria today is a shadow of the former heart of the Austro-Hungarian Empire that, at its height from 1867, was one of the greatest states of Europe. This was era of the 'Dual Monarchy' and famous for its lavish coinage, the korona and the filler. After defeat in the First World War, the empire collapsed in 1918 and Austria and Hungary went their separate ways.

From 1928 gold 25, 50 and 100 schilling coins were struck as commemoratives. And until 1937, Austria minted the silver thaler with the head of the Empress Maria Theresa. The coins are, oddly, dated 1780 which was the year of her death. Thalers were so popular – especially in Arab countries – that they were also minted in London, Bombay and even in Leningrad until 1975. It's estimated that some 800 million thalers have been struck.

PHILHARMONIC

Austrian coins were suppressed in 1938 after it was absorbed into Nazi Germany. And in 1945 when coin production started again, schillings made from aluminium made their appearance. But as Austria recovered and re-discovered sound money as well as its cultural heritage, a series of Gold 200 and 2000 schilling coins were struck annually from 1989 until 1999 to support the world-famous Vienna Philharmonic Orchestra… these were known, of course, and valued by collectors everywhere, as 'Philharmonics'.

DUCAT

The Hapsburgs developed the famous large silver coins in the 15th century known as guldengroschen and thaler (from whence we get the name 'dollar'). But the gold ducat, introduced at the same time, became one of the most popular coins for international trade even until the 20th century, when its purity and reputation made it acceptable almost everywhere in the world.

THE GOLD COINS OF AUSTRIA

THE COINS OF MODERN EUROPE

With thousands of years of history behind them, the traditional precious metal coins of the various states of Europe continue to excite and fascinate collectors. Many are from counties that no longer exist, some from nations that disappeared and have returned again. And of course, the greatest event in currency history has been the adoption of the Euro in most of Europe since January 1st 1999. Switzerland continues on its own independent path, as does Great Britain, and precious metal coins from these nations continue to be highly popular. But even the Euro has found its way into the ranks of the bullion coin…

SWISS VRENELI

The Swiss 'Vreneli' is one of the last mainland European survivors of the ancient precious metal coinage traditions. Vreneli is the informal name of the Tete d'Helvetia or Helvetiakopf (Head of Helvetia), legal tender in Switzerland and is minted in Bern in 10, 20 and 100 Swiss Franc face values with millesimal fineness of 900. The image of the goddess Helvetia gives it its 'Head' name – and sometimes it's known colloquially as the 'Swiss Miss'. The coins were issued between 1897 and 1936, and then again in 1947 and 1949. The 20 Franc coin is the most popular bullion coin.

THE GOLD EURO

Gold Euros have been issued by various countries primarily as bullion or commemorative coins. They have been issued in a variety of face values, from as little as .25 Euros (from France) right up to a €100,000 Euro coin from Austria, but the most common are €10, €20 and €100 face values. Curiously, the coins are only legal tender in the country that issues the coin, rather than in the rest of the EU, going against the principle of the Euro itself. However, as these beautiful coins are worth vastly more than their face values, they only appeal to collectors.

THE KRUGERRAND

The world's first major bullion coin of recent times, the Krugerrand, is 1 troy ounce (33.3 grams) of 22-carat gold. Designed by Otto Schultz, it bears the face of Boer leader Paul Kruger, and on the reverse side an image of a springbok. First minted in 1967 to help market South African gold, the coin was immediately popular.

By 1980 the Krugerrand accounted for 90% of global gold coin production. More than 6 million Krugerrands have been produced – yet, because of its one-troy-ounce weight, it remains hugely popular with collectors of bullion coins.

Perhaps most famous for the Krugerrand from the legendary gold fields of South Africa, the rest of the continent has a long history of gold coinage, stretching back to the days of ancient Egypt and Carthage, followed by the Islamic Caliphate and the Barbary States of the 14th century. Central and Southern Africa, such as the Gold Coast, what is now Tanzania, the old Belgian Congo and the British colonies of East Africa all contributed to this fascinating history.

In 1916, gold from the Kironda mine in German East Africa was coined as 15 rupee pieces, known as Tabora Sovereigns. Many African states have produced some of the most beautiful coins based on the flora and fauna of Africa. In 2001 Sierra Leone released 'The Big Five', a set of five large silver coins showing a rhinoceros, lion, leopard, elephant and buffalo on the reverses.

THE GOLD COINS OF AFRICA

For thousands of years China used the distinctive round coins with square holes, known as 'cash', shown on pages 10 and 11, as well as 'Sycee' ingots of poured metal.

Locally struck, not cast, coinages appeared from 1888, using gold, silver, copper and other metals. The process was moved forwards by the establishment in 1905 of the Tianjin mint, which created the dies for dozens of provincial mints, which in turn created a huge variety of coins.

The Imperial dragon was seen on some of the first coins at the end of the 19th century, and in 1988 it reappeared on a 100 Yuan gold coin and a 10 Yuan silver coin to celebrate the Lunar Year of the Dragon. The silver series had begun in 1983 with a coin featuring two pigs, and the gold series proper was initiated in 1997, the Year of the Ox.

These coins can be found in round shapes, in fan-like arcs, in rectangles, and in scalloped shapes like the beauty shown opposite and the silver coins below.

The coin most often associated with modern China is the Panda, which comes in both silver and gold, both typically .999 purity. The image of the Panda itself, like that of the Australian Kangaroo, changes every year, creating great interest for collectors, and Panda lovers. The Panda had started as a humble brass coin in 1983, it then fluctuated between copper and silver, before its formal elevation to precious metal status - it's even theoretically possible to find the Panda as a 10,000 Yuan gold coin weighing over 154 ounces.

The more portable 100 Yuan Gold Panda is generally available in graded form from Rosland - please ask what we have in stock.

COINS OF THE MIDDLE EAST

The ancient states of the Middle East have always held gold and precious metals in high regard, due in part to the constant political instability that has caused 'safe haven' metals such as gold to be constantly sought-after. Gold coins are easily transportable… and when the need arises, easily hidden… assets that can survive the upheavals that continue to this day.

ISRAEL

The modern state of Israel has been a prolific producer of commemorative and bullion coins, many showing biblical themes.

JORDAN

The ancient Hashemite Kingdom of Jordan has produced some of the region's most beautiful coins. Jordanian gold dinars have been minted since 1969.

ARABIA

Under the early caliphs, Arabia relied on gold and silver coins brought to Mecca by the faithful. The silver dirham evolved in 698AD to become the standard coin of the Islamic world for five centuries.

PALESTINE

Under Byzantine rule, Arab mints were established in Jerusalem striking Ikhshidid dinars and the famous gold bezant of Acre, which were copied around the Arab world.

THE GULF STATES

The gold and precious metal coins of Bahrain, Kuwait, Oman and Qatar are always popular. Commemorative gold coins are often issued, marking anniversaries and state occasions.

LEBANON

Lebanon hosted the Lake Placid Winter Olympics in 1980, and to mark this special event, the Banque du Liban produced a sought-after series of gold and silver commemoratives.

IRAQ

Once known as Mesopotamia, Iraq was famous for gold dinars from the Saddam Hussein period that are considered highly collectible. The 50 dinar issued in 1989 is one of the most valuable.

GOLD COINS OF THE WORLD

In response to enquiries from customers, we're now able able to offer the great gold coins of the world in a handsome wooden case, with each coin protected inside its own plastic case. This is a great way to start your collection, or to give it a new centerpiece. The coins we make available in this way are typically MS69 and MS70, the highest grades money can buy. Our Representatives will be happy to talk you through what we have in stock.

For illustration purposes, the photograph opposite shows the following coins, as graded and encapsulated by the Professional Coin Grading Service (PCGS):

* £100 Britannia	2015 MS69	.9999 fine gold
* $50 Canadian Maple Leaf	2015 MS69	.9999
* A$100 Australian Kangaroo	2015 MS70	.9999
* $50 American Buffalo	2015 MS70	.9999
* €100 Austrian Philharmonic	2015 MS69	.9999
* € 200 Germany	2002 MS70	.9999
* South African Krugerrand	2015 MS70	.917
* 500 Yuan Chinese Gold Panda	2015 MS70	.999

THE ALLURE
OF SILVER

While gold remains the most sought-after of the precious metals, silver has always had a special place in bullion history. A little more common than gold, silver remains more affordable. Yet gleaming and hard-wearing silver is, in many collector's eyes, every bit as beautiful as yellow gold.

Silver was known as 'argentum' in ancient times, meaning 'white' or 'shining'. Mentioned in the Book of Genesis, slag heaps found on islands in the Aegean Sea show silver was being extracted from lead as early as the 4th century BC. The Romans made silver their basic currency. An estimated stock of 10,000 tons of silver was circulating in the Roman economy, significantly more than all the silver circulating in medieval Europe. The Chinese were equally enthusiastic, and it became their main currency too.

But silver has had other, darker uses. It has excellent electrical conducting properties. During the Second World War, the US government 'loaned' almost its entire silver bullion reserve to the Manhattan Project, the world's first atom bomb, where it replaced a shortage of copper. After the war, the silver was melted back down and the silver was returned to the US Federal Reserve.

THE PEACE SILVER DOLLAR

This curiously-named coin resulted from a competition to find emblems of peace in post First World War America. The winner was designer Anthony de Francisci, showing a bald eagle at rest clutching an olive branch with the legend 'Peace.' Minted between 1921 to 1928, and again in 1934 and 1935, it was the last US dollar coin to be struck for circulation in silver. In 1965, 300,000 Peace silver dollars were struck bearing a 1964 date, but these were never issued and are believed to have been melted down.

THE MORGAN SILVER DOLLAR

The Morgan Silver Dollar was first minted between 1878 and 1904, and again in 1921. Named after its designer, George T Morgan, these coins were designed to 'give Miss Liberty back her femininity' with a much more flattering image of Liberty on the obverse. In the 1960s, a large quantity of uncirculated Morgan dollars was found in the US Treasury vaults and released for sale to collectors.

WHY ARE 'PREMIUM' COINS OF INTEREST?

Premium coins exist in many different varieties — including numismatics and graded coins. Regardless of their metallic make-up, design, or minted value, one thing they have in common is they're not raw "bullion." Every day, bullion is minted in vast quantities all around the world, and its value is dependent on the value of the metal on the day you want to buy or sell it. With premium coins you get the metal content, of course, but many people find the other attractions of premium coins to be more compelling than current market pricing of their metal content.

A great contemporary example of a premium coin is Rosland's limited mintage 2015 Canadian Maple Leaf. A beautiful coin minted in honour of Fisher House Foundation — an organization that provides free lodging for the family members of service people and veterans undergoing hospital treatment. Along with the added attraction that each coin sold meant more money for Fisher House, the 2015 Canadian Maple Leaf's heart-shaped "mint mark" helped make it a unique collectible.

In the pages ahead you'll read about a selection of premium coins available from Rosland. They include pieces from across the world and across the centuries – Roman coins, treasure from the bottom of the sea, beautiful limited edition coin sets, and exclusive offerings like the Formula 1® Collection and the Lady Liberty series. We add new inventory whenever we find something we think our customers will love, so please ask one of our Gold Specialists what's available today.

Officially Licensed by Formula One World Championship Limited

Rosland is proud to offer this gold and silver collection celebrating the most prestigious and glamorous motor racing event in the world, the FIA Formula One World Championship.

The Formula 1 Coin Collection includes a unique new series of 1/4 oz. coins in 999.9 fine gold, commemorating four of the most well-known F1 races:

- Formula 1 British Grand Prix
- Formula 1 Gran Premio D'Italia
- Formula 1 United States Grand Prix
- Formula 1 Grande Prêmio do Brasil

GRAN PREMIO D'ITALIA™

UNITED STATES GRAND PRIX™

GRANDE PRÊMIO DO BRASIL™

BRITISH GRAND PRIX™

SILVERSTONE
BUDAPEST
YAS MARINA
SAKHIR
SHANGHAI
SOCHI
CATALUNYA
MONZA
SINGAPORE
SÃO PAULO
MEXICO CITY
SPIELBERG
AUSTIN
Formula 1
999.9 FINE GOLD
ONE KILO

The 2016 collection also features all 21 Formula 1 circuit names on Kilo and 2.5 oz gold coins, and on 2.5 oz silver coins.

All the coins in the F1 collection are 2016 issue, legal tender proofs minted by Swiss-based PAMP S.A. in strictly limited editions. The 2.5 oz silver coin, shown below, is .999 silver, while all the gold coins, including the kilo coin opposite and the 2.5 oz below are 999.9 fine gold.

UNIQUE COLLECTIBLES, ONLY FROM ROSLAND

ROSLAND EXCLUSIVE: LADY LIBERTY SERIES

Rosland is offering a new series of legal tender, 1/4 oz. proof gold coins, with metal fineness of 999.9. These exclusive coins are minted by Swiss-based, world-renowned PAMP S.A., which stands for 'Produits Artistiques Métaux Prècieux'.

The first design, minted for the first time in 2015 and shown opposite offers a close-up of the Statue of Liberty, in relief, with different frosted finishes on a proof-quality mirror background. Joining this design in the 2016 series are the unique perspectives you'll see below.

The obverse of each coin features Ian Rank-Broadley's classic portrait of Queen Elizabeth II with frosted finish on a proof-quality mirror background, together with the 25 dollar legal tender value of the coin.

Each coin is sealed within a package showing the Lady Liberty design on the front, while the back shows the coin's certificate number, its proof quality, the metal's purity, the coin's weight and the signature of PAMP's assayer.

Certificate Number	000001
Metal Fineness	Au 999.9
Metal Weight	1/4 oz
Quality	Proof

  Certificate Assayer

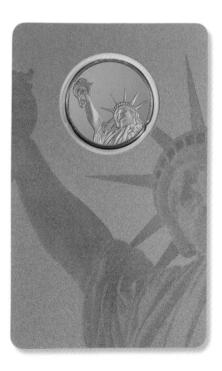

ANCIENT TREASURES - THE SEVEN HILLS HOARD

The Roman coins from what is called the The Seven Hills Hoard spanned the reigns of the emperor Nero (54-68 AD) and the emperor Trebonianus Gallus (251-253 AD). Its contents are a cross-section of coins that circulated in the mid-3rd Century, ranging from freshly minted issues bearing the image of the reigning emperor to heavily worn pieces about two centuries old.

It's thought the coins were buried in the early to mid-250s AD, probably in a time of turmoil, almost certainly to prevent its discovery. The latest denarii in the hoard are those of Gordian III (225-244 AD), the last emperor to strike denarii for anything other than ceremonial purposes.

This group is what often is called a 'merchant's hoard' because it is made up of a variety of coin types that would have been encountered in commerce, rather than being a hoard limited to a new issue which might have been intended for a military or government payment.

The denarius was the standard silver coin of the Roman world for more than 450 years, from about 211 B.C. up through the early 240s AD. From the late 40s BC onward it was common for denarii to bear the portrait of their issuer, and it became standard practice after the Empire was founded in 27 B.C.

Thus, each of these denarii has on its obverse a portrait of a member of the ruling family. Quite often it is the reigning emperor; in other cases it is his wife, a child, a close relative or an heir-apparent. The inscriptions on the obverse provide the name and at least some of the titles held by the person portrayed. The obverse inscription is often continued onto the reverse. In other cases, the inscription on the reverse is separate and distinct from that on the obverse.

The reverses bear a variety of designs, though usually showing a god, goddess or other personification, often relating to victory in war or the success of the ruler.

Each of these coins was hand-struck, so the shapes of the coins can vary considerably. The style of engraving varies on these coins because each die was hand-cut by artisans with differing levels of skill. With coins from hoards there can be issues arising from exposure to the elements, and from preservation techniques, but this group of coins is regarded as being in relatively good, and consistent condition.

As befits a nation born along historical trade routes, the coins first circulated in what is now Russia were a combination of Viking, Anglo-Saxon and Roman coins, with Byzantine gold being especially valued.

The first locally-minted coins, other than imitations of foreign coinage, were struck in the 11th century, in the Principality of Kiev, but for many centuries after that foreign coins were widely used. Many of these coins, both gold and silver, were melted down into ingots. Fascinatingly, the modern Russian word rouble, or ruble, is believed to derive from the practice of cutting these ingots in half and the Russian verb *rubit*, meaning 'to cut'.

Peter the Great modernised the Russian currency in the late 17th Century, with the introduction of large silver rouble coins showing the ruler on one side and the Imperial eagle on the other. This design approach lasted till the end of the Tsarist period in Russia.

Rosland is proud to offer graded 5 Rouble coins from 1898, bearing the bust of Tsar Nicholas II, facing left, on the obverse. Nicholas II ruled from 1894 till 1917, when he was forced to abdicate, though he only appeared on coins from 1895 to 1915, and after 1911 gold coinage was suspended in Russia. The reverse of the coin shows the crowned, double-headed Imperial eagle, with ribbons on the crown. These 5 double coins were produced at the St. Petersburg mint without a mint mark.

RUSSIAN GOL ROUBLES

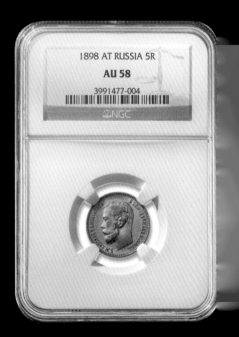

NOVEMBER 2012:
The Royal Canadian Mint stuns the world by announcing
THE 'CANADA HOARD'

In late November 2012, the Royal Canadian Mint made a wholly unexpected announcement that astonished bullion coin dealers and collectors around the world.

They had been holding large quantities of 1912 to 1914 $5 and $10 gold coins since the outbreak of the First World War, hidden deep in the vaults of the Bank of Canada since 1935 as part of Canada's gold reserve. The hoard totalled some 245,000 individual coins, with the majority of them $10 face value coins. The coins were made of 90% pure Canadian gold, much of it from the Klondike region. But of the hoard, 30,000 had been hand-picked by Canadian Mint officials to be released as high-quality coins… and the rest, bearing imperfections from handling or environmental conditions, were to be melted down and turned into valuable if unexciting gold bars.

Rosland have secured a number of $5 and $10 gold coins from this Canada Hoard. The coins feature the crowned head of George V, who was still King of the Dominion of Canada, and the Canadian Coat of Arms. This is a very limited coin and because of its historical interest, as well as the small quantities available, collectors around the world are paying some very interesting prices.

THE **SS *REPUBLIC*** TREASURE:

On 25th October 1865, the SS *Republic*, a thousand-ton paddle driven steamship, foundered in a hurricane off the coast of Savannah, Georgia, and went to the bottom.

She had left New York on October 18, bound for New Orleans. She was carrying passengers and a cargo of $400,000 in coins, mostly in gold $10 and $20 pieces, intended for use as hard currency after the Civil War. On the fifth day of her voyage, a hurricane off the coast of Georgia proved too strong for the ship. At 4 pm on October 25, 1865, she sank. The passengers and crew escaped in four lifeboats and a makeshift raft, but it was not until two days later, on October 27 that the survivors, now desperate with thirst, were found by the sailing ship Horace Beals. The passengers were transferred and taken to Charleston. Most of the passengers and crew survived, although several were lost on the raft before they could be rescued. But all the coins were lost.

In August 2003, the wreck of the *Republic* was located by Odyssey Marine Exploration. She was found about 100 miles (160 km) southeast of Savannah, Georgia, in about 1,700 feet (500 metres) of water. A salvage effort recovered about one-third of the rare 19th century gold and silver coins carried aboard… over 51,000 US gold and silver coins worth an estimated $75 million. The search and recovery effort was depicted in a National Geographic Society TV documentary 'Civil War Gold'.

The salvaged treasure included numerous $20 Double Eagles, $10 Eagles, silver half dollars and even a few silver quarter dollars. All of the coins have been professionally conserved by Numismatic Conservation Services (NCS) and graded by Numismatic Guaranty Corporation (NGC). A wide variety of dates and mints ranging from the 1840's to 1865 have been documented in this remarkable hoard, including many of the finest-known examples of United States gold and silver coins from the period.

Rosland has secured a limited number of authentic coins from the SS *Republic* which are now available to Rosland clients in box sets.

Watch the fascinating story on YouTube.

Gold and Silver salvaged from the b of the ocean

A limited number of coins from the
SS *Republic* treasure are available through
Rosland, presented in boxed collector cases

LIMITED EDITION COINS: FIVE PORTRAITS OF HER MAJESTY

On the page opposite you'll see the glorious detail on these coins – four portraits of the Queen that have appeared on UK circulating coins over the course of her reign. The design is based on the work of Mary Gillick (1953), Arnold Machin (1971), Raphael Maklouf (1985) and Ian Rank-Broadley (1998).

The official design name is 'Four Portraits' but the obverse bears a fifth image of the Queen. This new portrait was commissioned by our friends at the Commonwealth Mint and designed by American artist Joel Iskowitz, who's very well regarded for his work for the U.S. Mint.

This wonderful legal tender coinage was minted in both .999 silver and in .999 fine gold, but in strictly limited quantities. Only 1000 of the 5 Troy ounce silver proofs with a £5 face value were produced in 2015, while only 100 of the rarest form were minted – the £100 denomination, 1 Troy ounce gold 'Satin Proof'. All these coins come with a numbered certificate and are presented in a handsome black gloss box. If you can bear to give one of these as a gift, all you'll need is a ribbon.

ONE HUNDRED POUNDS

HER MAJESTY QUEEN ELIZABETH II · DG

In Greek myths the Graces were the daughters of Zeus and Eurynome; Homer described them as part of Aphrodite's retinue. They're sometimes known as Splendour, Mirth and Good Cheer, sometimes as Beauty, Charm and Joy, and they've been a part of art and culture for thousands of years. The Three Graces are nearly always depicted embracing or dancing together, though they can be portrayed naked or classically robed.

This particular vision of the Three Graces was inspired by a design sculpted by Royal Mint Chief Engraver William Wyon (1795 - 1851). What makes his Graces most distinctive is that they also serve to represent Ireland, England, and Scotland. On the left of the design is a harp to symbolise Ireland, on the right is a thistle to evoke Scotland, while the central figure is garlanded with English roses and has a shield bearing the Union flag.

These beautiful legal tender coins are minted from .999 fine gold in proof and matte proof versions, with 1 ounce and 1/10 ounce coins being produced in 2015, but only in very limited quantities. Each coin has a unique identifying number and a quality grade assigned by leading independent certifiers, NGC, and is presented in a fine black gloss box.

LIMITED EDITION COIN THE 'THREE GRACES'

LIMITED EDITION COINS: CELEBRATING OUR LONGEST-REIGNING MONARCH

This new set of Sovereign coins commemorates Queen Elizabeth II becoming Britain's longest-reigning Monarch, taking on the position formerly held by Queen Victoria, her great-great-grandmother.

The coins echo the design of a £5 gold coin, known as 'Una and the Lion', minted in 1839 to celebrate the accession of Queen Victoria in 1837. The young Queen is portrayed as a character from Edmund Spenser's poem *The Faerie Queen*, first published in 1590. This was the first time a British monarch had been depicted as a fictional person.

The choice of Spenser's Lady Una is laden with symbolism, beyond the poem's treatment of Una as a personification of the 'True Church' as Elizabethans understood it, and as a representative of Truth as a supreme virtue. In the poem, Una travels with the Red Cross knight, who represents England and embodies the virtue of Holiness. She becomes separated from the knight, George, and while resting on the ground she's nearly eaten by a savage lion. The beast is so amazed by her loveliness that he becomes her protector instead. By analogy the power and dignity of Britain was blissfully in thrall to the young Queen Victoria.

This unique set offers the 'Elizabeth and the Lion' sovereign in three sizes - the full sovereign, the half-sovereign and the quarter-sovereign. Each set comes with a numbered certificate of authenticity and is presented in a handsome black box.

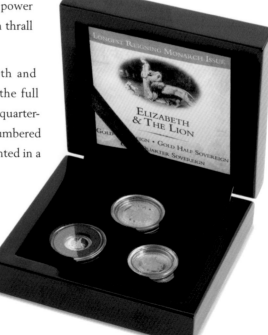

SOVEREIGN

HER MAJESTY

2015

LIMITED EDITION COINS: HENRY VIII, 500 YEARS ON.

We're delighted to have secured the last of a limited edition of 250 sets of .916 gold coins minted in 2009 to celebrate the accession of Henry VIII in 1509.

The design features a striking, front-facing portrait of the king, along with a symbolic Tudor rose, combining the white rose of York and the red rose of Lancaster. The first English Sovereign coin was minted in 1489, during the reign of Henry VIII's father, Henry VII, born Harri Tudur, founder of the Tudor line.

Henry came to the throne with a sizeable inheritance from his fiercely frugal father, but his spending on palaces, ships, weapons, and overseas adventures led to difficulties. Cardinal Wolsey debased the currency, and Thomas Cromwell took the practice further. This helped balance the books but created inflation and seriously damaged the economy. There may be lessons here for modern times.

In this boxed set there's an exquisite quarter sovereign, a half sovereign and a full sovereign, presented together with a numbered certificate, and they're legal tender, 'investment-grade' gold, exempt from VAT.

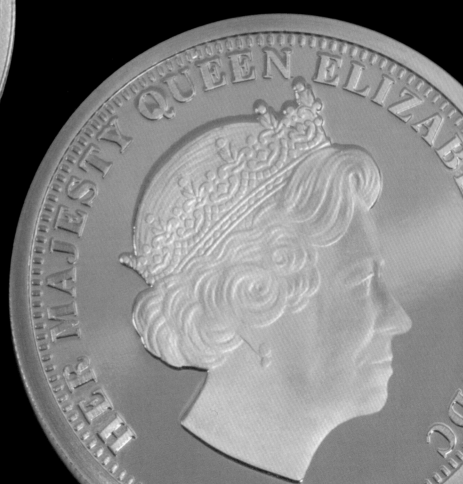

WHAT SHOULD YOU LOOK FOR IN PRECIOUS COINS?

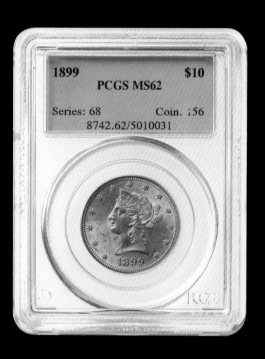

1899 $10

PCGS MS62

Series: 68   Coin. 156
8742.62/5010031

You can, of course, choose to invest in ordinary gold or silver coins. The problem is that one of the most important features of a coin... and the key to its value... is its condition. If you see cheap coins being advertised, they are almost certainly what we call 'ungraded'.

Collectors will always pay a significant premium for coins in outstanding condition. That's why professional 'grading' is so important to the collector.

'Grading' is done by an independent grading organization. They inspect every single coin minutely, and each coin is given its grade - between 1 and 70. 70 means a perfect coin with a full strike and no marking whatsoever (rare, of course, but Rosland can supply them), and 1 means a barely identifiable coin.

There are five critical elements that define the grade:

1 *The surface condition:* the number of marks and scratches on the surface and the severity of these.

2 *Strike:* how strongly the design is stamped onto the coin.

3 *Coloration/Toning:* how much the coin has changed from its original color. Any discoloration could be due to age, improper cleaning, storage, or handling of the coin (even natural oils from one's fingers will lower the grade rating). Some degree of toning can be seen as a sign that coins have not been cleaned or polished – polishing can reduce a coin to 'jewelry grade'.

4 *Lustre:* how much of the original shine is still intact.

5 *Eye appeal:* a general category that incorporates all of the above elements.

Presently the NGC (Numismatic Guaranty Corporation) and PCGS (Professional Coin Grading Service) form the top tier of a three tier grading service. They guarantee the grades and authenticity of the coins. Although ungraded coins are usually cheaper, they can be a risky purchase. The true value of a coin lies in having it graded correctly, by an established and knowledgeable coin grading service. Rosland only uses NGC and PCGS for coin-grading.

Once the coin is graded, it is then sonically sealed in a clear, tamper-proof holder - a 'slab'. Anti-counterfeiting measures include a holographic emblem on the back, the design of which has changed over time (for example, the current PCGS design depicts the name "PCGS" and a Saint-Gaudens Double Eagle). On the front, the coin information provided includes its type, denomination, grade, and a unique serial number assigned to that particular coin, as well as a machine-readable barcode. PCGS maintains a census of all coins they have graded since their inception, revealing the incidence of each date, mint mark, and reported variety of coin.

COMMONLY USED COIN GRADES

Abb.	Grade	Description
P-1	Poor	Barely identifiable; must have date and mintmark.
FR-2	Fair	Worn almost smooth, but lacking the damage 'Poor' coins possess
G-4	Good	Heavily worn. Inscriptions may have merged into the rims in places; exact details are mostly gone.
VG-8	Very Good	Very worn, but all major design elements are clear, if maybe faint. But little, if any, central detail.
F-12	Fine	Very worn, but wear is even and overall design elements stand out clearly. Almost fully-separated rims.
VF-20	Very Fine	Moderately worn, with some finer details remaining. All letters should be readable. Full, clean rims.
EF-40	Extremely Fine	Lightly worn; all devices are clear, major devices clear & bold.
AU-50	About Uncirculated	Slight traces of wear on high points; may have contact marks and little eye appeal.
AU-58	Very Choice About Uncirculated	Slightest hints of wear marks, no major contact marks, almost full lustre (quality of shine), and positive eye appeal.
MS-60	Mint State Basal	Strictly uncirculated but that's all; ugly coin with no lustre, also with obvious contact marks, etc.
MS-63	Mint State Acceptable	Uncirculated, but with contact marks and nicks, slightly impaired lustre, but overall appealing appearance. The strike is average to weak.
MS-65	Mint State Choice	Uncirculated with strong lustre, very few contact marks, but excellent eye appeal. The strike is above average.
MS-68	Mint State Premium Quality	Uncirculated with perfect lustre, no visible contact marks to the naked eye, with exceptional eye appeal. The strike is sharp and attractive.
MS-69	Mint State All-But-Perfect	Uncirculated with perfect lustre, sharp, attractive strike, and very exceptional eye appeal. A perfect coin except for microscopic flaws (8x magnification) in planchet (pre-strike), strike, or contact marks.
MS-70	Mint State Perfect	The perfect coin. There are no microscopic flaws visible to 8x, the strike is sharp, perfectly-centred, and on a flawless planchet. The coin is bright, full, original lustre and outstanding eye appeal.

Graded coins come in sealed, protective transparent containers called 'slabs' to preserve the beauty and quality of the coin.

Where does gold come from?

Current scientific thinking is that all the gold in the universe comes from the violent collision of neutron stars, as shown in the illustration opposite, creating a black hole and throwing out enormous quantities of heavy metals, including gold. All the gold present in our planet's initial composition is now thousands of miles beneath us, at the earth's core. There's believed to be enough down below to carpet the surface of the Earth to a depth of 1.6 feet, but that belief is unlikely to be tested.

Through the whole of human history less than 200,000 tones have been mined, with 65% mined since 1950, and 90% since the California Gold Rush. In January 2011, the US Geological Society estimated that there were only 51,000 tones of known supply left to us. All of this is believed to have come to the Earth from meteorites striking the planet's surface over the millennia, being shuffled downwards by geological upheavals and tectonic movements, beyond the force of gravity. The result is that it's increasingly expensive, and a major undertaking, to mine gold. For instance, 126 mines opened around the world between 2004 and 2013; the average development time, before mining began, was 17 years.

Naturally, mining is influenced by demand levels and prices, so responding to market conditions, mining increased on average by 4.7% per year between 2008, a 10-year low point, and 2013. That growth has now nearly leveled off, and is unlikely to resume in the short term.

The other source of gold is recycling, especially jewellery, but also coins and industrial metal. With a commodity as precious as gold, no one knowingly throws it away. As much as 26% of the available gold supply in 2014 came from recycling, down from the peak level of 42%, or 1,728 metric tons, in 2009. That peak was driven by the price of gold, but it's worth considering that those 1,728 tons represented only around 1% of all the above-surface gold in the world. Most gold stays where it is, in the form it's in, nearly all the time.

The big producers today are China, Australia and the US, with 13.1%, 9.2% and 9.1% respectively, but US production is in decline, along with that of Ghana and Indonesia. China's expanding, with its 600+ domestic mines, as are countries including Mongolia and Argentina.

We started this page on the macro scale, so we can close it with a very big number. The World Gold Council have calculated that, as one ounce of gold can be drawn out into a wire 50 miles long, all the gold ever mined could be wrapped around the Earth 11.2 million times. Again, this theory is not about to be tested.

Sources: University of Bristol; US Geological Survey; NASA; World Gold Council; Boston Consulting Group; Goldfacts.org; Wired.

The Earliest Methods of Extraction - 'Placer' Mining

The term 'placer' comes from the Spanish *placer*, meaning alluvial or sand deposit, so placer mining is essentially the mining of alluvial (stream bed) deposits for gold or other precious minerals, though other circumstances can apply.

TYPES OF PLACER GOLD DEPOSIT

Type	Description
Alluvial	Gold moved by water from its original location and mixed in silt with other minerals.
Residual	Gold found at the site of a lode, not washed away by water.
Bench	Typically gold found in an old, dry stream bed at an elevated location, including mountain tops.

METHODS OF PLACER GOLD EXTRACTION

Method	Description
Panning	This is the image we all have of mountain men sifting pans of gold by hand. In practice it was mainly used to locate deposits, at which point other technology would be used.
Rocker Box	This is a simple device to wash water across a dirt and rock sample, to separate the heavier gold ore.
Sluice Box	These range from the simplest wooden devices to modern metal frames, but the principal is the same - running water does the work.
Dry Washing	This is commonly done where there's no ready supply of water - in dry stream beds at altitude, for example - and makes use of air to do water's work.
Trommel	A rotating metal tube fed with water and ore.
Underground Mining	This is commonly done once the surface deposits have been worked out. In Siberia and Alaska fire is still used to soften frozen ground so digging can take place. The frozen nature of the surrounding ground makes it relatively safe to mine.
Hydraulic Mining	The use of water on a large scale for gold extraction dates from the Roman Era. It's a technique that works best in hilly country, where floods, or later jets, of water can wash the soil from whole hillsides.

California's Gold and Cornwall's contribution

California was associated with gold long before the Gold Rush. Its name is believed to come from an early 16th century Spanish romance, *Las Sergas (Adventures) de Esplandián*, which described an island populated by Amazon (women) warriors who used gold weapons, ruled by Queen Calafia. Spanish explorers of the Pacific applied the name to what's now the Baja California Peninsula, which was then thought to be an island.

Gold, and the search for cities made from it, was a major factor in Spanish exploration and conquest, along with silver, with both exported to the Old World in vast quantities, but California's importance as a source of gold didn't become known till after its Spanish rulers had given way to the Americans.

California's gold had been distributed by the action of tectonic plates. The Pacific Plate moved beneath the North American Plate, generating enormous heat, melting compounds rich in metals and forcing them into fissures between rocks being formed above. This meant thousands of veins of gold were created in California's granite mountains. The action of water over millennia broke down some of the deposits and carried them towards the sea.

The discovery of gold dust at a saw mill in California in 1848 led to a worldwide explosion of interest, and a flood of prospectors and optimists who followed the traces of gold back to their roots in the Sierras.

We've come to associate the California Gold Rush with solitary prospectors working their stake on a mountain stream's course, but fairly early on the labor became collective and then corporately run, as the gold became harder to reach and more capital investment was needed. One man can pan for placer gold, but it takes a lot of men and money to follow the vein as it goes deep underground. Neither party is guaranteed success, of course.

Along with the Australians, Spanish and Chinese were a considerable number of skilled miners and mine supervisors from the Cornish tin mines*. They were mostly to be found in the northern Sierra, where the first Cornish pump was installed at the Gold Hill mine in 1855, and where Cornish-designed ore-crushing stamp mills were among the earliest built. They also imported the Cornish milling technique of blanket-washing - the use of specially-woven blankets to recover minute gold particles from the excavated material.

Many of the Cornish miners were employed by Cornish mine and mill managers, themselves employed by English investors keen to make their fortune, and reliant on their fellow-countrymen's expertise. They were well regarded by their American peers, but the admiration was not always a two-way street. A Cornish miner named W.E. Gill wrote in the Truro press in 1852 regarding milling - "Here some ability must be displayed in separating the gold without a loss, and here John [Bull] respectfully takes leave of Jonathan [Yank]".

Cornish miners also brought their traditional foods with them, and to this day there are Cornish pasty shops to be found in across the state border in Arizona - they were founded to feed the copper miners of the area in the nineteenth century.

(*Source: A Golden State. Mining and Economic Development in Gold Rush California. Editors James J. Rawls and Richard J. Orsi. University of California Press, 1999.)

WRESTING GOLD FROM THE GROUND:
The deepest mines in the world.

Some of the oldest known gold artifacts were found in the Varna Necropolis in Bulgaria. The graves of the necropolis were built between 4700 and 4200BC, indicating that gold mining could be at least 7000 years old. A group of German and Georgian archaeologists claims the Sakdrisi site in southern Georgia, dating to the 3rd or 4th millennium BC, may be the world's oldest known gold mine.

The Romans used hydraulic mining methods, such as sluicing on a large scale to extract gold from extensive alluvial deposits, such as those at Las Medulas. In the UK, there is only one known Roman gold mine – Dolaucothi in west Wales. Gold was a prime motivation for the campaign in Dacia, when the Romans invaded Transylvania in what is now Romania in the 2nd century AD.

In India, gold was first mined prior to the 2nd and 3rd century AD by digging small pits. The metal continued to be mined by the eleventh century kings of South India, the Vijayanagara Empire from 1336 to 1560, and later by Tipu Sultan, the king of Mysore state and the British.

During the 19th century, numerous gold rushes in remote regions around the globe caused large migrations of miners, such as the California Gold Rush of 1849, the Victorian Gold Rush, and the Klondike Gold Rush. The discovery of gold in the Witwatersrand led to the Second Boer War and the founding of South Africa.

Today, much of the world's gold comes from hard rock mining. This process extracts gold encased in rock, rather than fragments in loose sediment. Sometimes open-pit mining is used, such as at the Fort Knox Mine in central Alaska. Barrick Gold Corporation has one of the largest open-pit gold mines in North America, located on its Goldstrike mine property in northeastern Nevada. South Africa has the world's deepest hard rock gold mine – up to 3,900 metres (12,800 ft) underground. At such depths, the heat is unbearable for humans, and air conditioning is required for the safety of the workers. The first such mine to receive air conditioning was Robinson Deep, at that time the deepest mine in the world for any mineral.

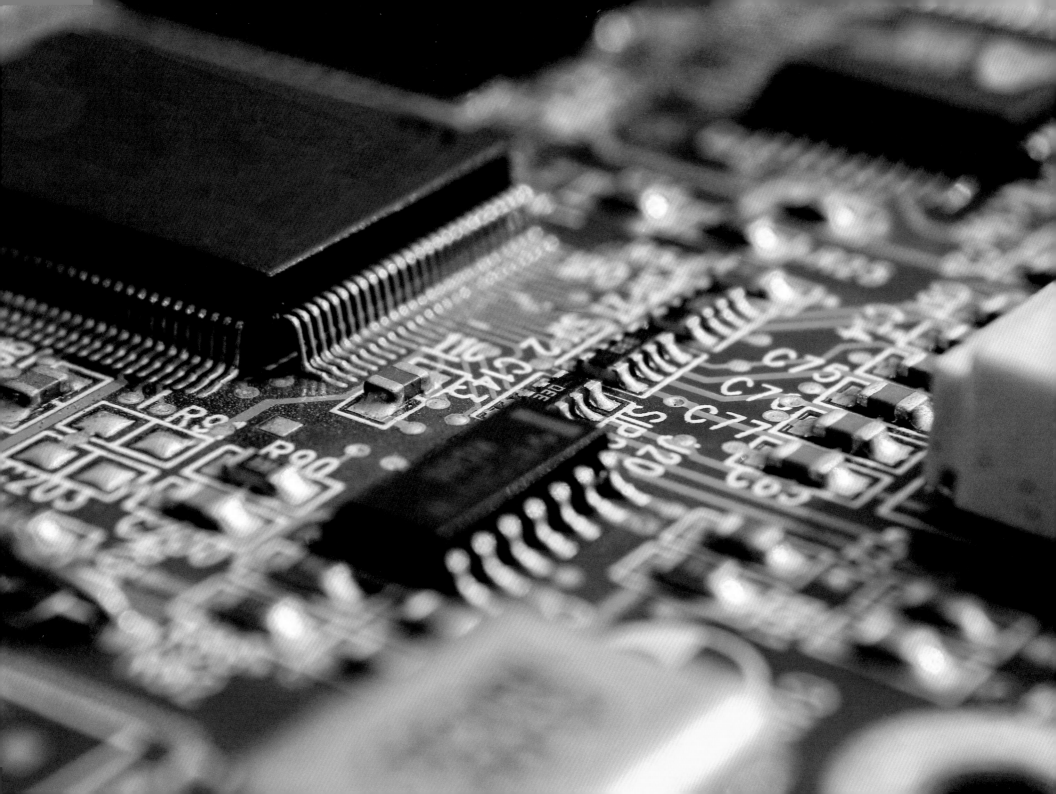

HOW GOLD MAKES YOUR PHONE SMART:
Gold in technology

Modern technology has discovered new uses for gold that would make the ancients covet the precious metal even more.

With all the mined gold in the world since the beginning of time estimated to fill a cube just 20 metres on each side, gold will always be rare and precious. But new technology has created new demand for gold. It doesn't tarnish or corrode, even dumped in sea water. It's an outstanding conductor of electricity, so where tiny electrical currents need to be transmitted with minimum loss, gold is perfect. And it can be made so thin that it becomes almost transparent.

These rare properties mean that satellites, mobile phones, computers and advanced electronics now need gold in ever greater quantities. Indeed, many examples of modern technology would simply not be possible without tiny amounts of gold. Your smart phone, for instance, contains microscopic amounts of gold without which its complex internal circuitry would simply not work.

Nanotechnology is the next great breakthrough. It builds electronic circuits at the atomic level – circuits that may be just a few atoms thick. Once again, gold makes this possible. Gold's ability to hold its properties, even at this thinness, makes it vital as this technology moves forward. Gold is helping in medicine, too, where it's being used to build highly-targeted drugs for the human body. Gold is also being used to create conducting plastics, to make specialised pigments, and advanced catalysts which can purify water or air.

From the mask of Tutankhamun to your smart phone, gold is one of the greatest metals known to man. Gold never corrodes. It never rusts away, not even after a million years. Eternal, solid, precious: no wonder these days so many sensible people continue to put their trust in gold.

Annual Gold price 1995 to present

What happens to the price of gold?

Gold has been used throughout history as money and has been a standard for currency until recent times. Many European countries used a 'Gold Standard' in the latter part of the 19th century until temporarily suspended during times of war.

After World War II, the Bretton Woods system pegged the US dollar to the price of gold at the rate of $35 per troy ounce until the so-called 'Nixon Shock' in 1971, when the US unilaterally suspended direct convertibility. The last currency to be uncoupled from gold was the Swiss Franc in 2000.

Since 1919, the most common benchmark for the price of gold has been the London Gold Fixing, a twice-daily telephone meeting of five members of the London bullion market. As gold is also traded around the world, there is also the intra-day 'spot price' calculated from over-the-counter trades.

Central banks and the IMF play an important role in the gold price. At the end of 2004, these organisations held 19% of all above-ground gold as official gold reserves. Both China and Russia in recent years have been building their reserves, and India has recently purchased over 200 tons of gold, which has led to a surge in prices.

Joe Foster, portfolio manager of New York based Van Eck International Gold Fund, said in 2010: "The currencies of all the major countries, including ours, are under severe pressure because of massive government deficits. The more money that is pumped into these economies – the printing of money basically – then the less valuable the currencies become." Under these circumstances, some economists argue, the demand for gold increases.

Certainly, over the last 20 years, the price of gold has shown remarkable growth, to an extent where it had become extremely expensive. There has been a correction in recent years, and the price of gold has now come back down to what many people regard as sensible levels where ordinary collectors or bullion buyers can afford to come back into the market.

Tax on Gold: VAT and CGT FREE

Gold coins have a unique advantage for collectors concerned about value and tax. From 1st January 2000, VAT was abolished on gold of a certain purity by Her Majesty's Revenue and Customs. And for British legal tender gold and silver coins there is total exemption from Capital Gains Tax.

Since 2000, there are many gold coins that are exempt from VAT. The ruling is straightforward: if a gold coin is 90% pure gold or above, then VAT does not apply. Given that VAT is currently 20%, it's an excellent deal for the collector looking to maximise value.

Coins such as British gold Sovereigns and Britannias, South African Krugerrands, American Saint-Gaudens, Liberties and Buffalos, and Canadian Maple Leaf bullion coins are therefore VAT free. In fact most gold bullion coins are included.

What this means, of course, is that almost all the gold coins featured in this book are totally free of VAT, which makes owning a beautiful British Gold Sovereign, or a US Buffalo, or a Canadian Maple Leaf even more enticing. You will have a precious piece of history in your possession, a supreme example of craftsmanship… but above all, you will also be able to congratulate yourself that you have snapped up an object that represents remarkable value for money.

Capital Gains Tax (CGT)

Everyone has an an annual exemption of £11,100 (as at 2015). But if you make a gain in excess of that, you must declare that profit and you will pay tax at the rate of 18% or 28% of the profit above that allowance (based on current HMRC rules). The rate you pay depends on your normal rate of tax.

Yet CGT on certain coins does not apply. Such coins must be British Legal Tender. Gold and silver Britannias as well as gold Sovereigns (among the most popular coins from Rosland) are legal tender at face value, though the value in gold far exceeds face value. So any legal tender UK coin is CGT free. Any gain you make when you sell can legally remain outside your CGT calculation, no matter how great it is.

Where to keep your gold?

From mattresses to bank vaults

One of the great attractions of gold is that you can see it, touch it, feel it. Gold is real. Gold is Gold. No wonder, over the years, some people have even hidden their gold under their mattress – not a storage option recommended by Rosland!

Rosland will normally arrange for delivery to your home and of course your gold is insured until it's handed over to you. A delivery date will always be set in advance. Once safely in your hands, you can of course choose your own storage method, but we do recommend a safe or a strong box.

The Rosland Buy Back Policy

Keeping your gold coins secure is one thing, but disposing of them is quite another

Naturally, there may come a time in the future when you wish to sell your collection of gold coins. Perhaps your circumstances have changed or your interests lead you in another direction. For whatever reason you wish to sell your gold coins, Rosland is always here to help. In fact, every time you buy gold coins from Rosland, they come with our 'Buy Back' Policy. It's very simple: whenever you want to sell coins you've purchased from us, we'll buy them back from you at our current bid price. This means you need never worry about buying something now that's difficult to dispose of later. With gold coins from Rosland you know you'll have an instant buyer for your coins whenever you choose to sell them.

CAN WE HELP? Your frequently-asked questions

We've helped thousands to start their precious metals collections. These are the questions most people want the answers to…

I like the idea of gold, but I'm also interested in silver - what would you recommend?

We believe everyone should make their own decisions, based on the best available information, so we'd recommend you take your time and consider your options. That said, for many people in the UK, gold coins are the more attractive option because there's no VAT payable, (provided they're of a certain level of purity, as is the case with the coins Rosland sells). There's also nothing quite like the feel of gold in your hand, or the way it catches the light and almost seems to glow from within. On the other hand, with silver you get a lot more for your money, so some people find it's a great way to get started for a limited outlay.

What exactly is 'bullion'?

The term 'bullion' applies to both bars and coins. Bars, or ingots, have to be 99.5% pure gold in the EU. They include the 'good delivery' bars used in the wholesale bullion market that can weigh up to 13kg! Bullion coins have to be at least 90% gold by law, though some have a fineness as high as .9999 gold, including some examples of the UK's own Britannia gold coin. Gold bullion coins of this purity are exempt from VAT, by the way. Just to make things more complicated, bullion coins can be made of gold, silver, platinum and palladium, but gold and silver suit most people well enough.

Why are 'numismatic' coins of interest?

Numismatic coins are perhaps best defined as 'older coins in limited supply'. Unlike modern bullion coins, which can be produced in unlimited mintages, the production run of older coins is of course a known quantity and availability is limited. These coins are often aesthetically and historically appealing, and they're commonly graded by third-party entities to establish a ranking of quality, all of which allows a market to arise in which numismatic coins can have values much greater than their worth in gold. These coins can have considerable value, as well as giving great pleasure as objects of beauty.

How will I know I've received what I've ordered?

When you receive your order it will come with a list of the contents. The order will have been checked by a third party, but you should take a close look and call us if you have any doubts. With graded and numismatic coins, each one will be separately packaged in a tamper-proof plastic case, or 'slab', by the grading company who assessed it. Each coin has a unique bar-code identifier and a description of the coin, using the terms outlined in this book and a score on the 0-70 'Sheldon Scale'. This should make everything clear, but again, call us if you're unsure.

FIRST PUBLISHED IN JULY 2014

Fourth Edition. Printed July 2017.

The actual size of coins is not necessarily indicated by images in this book. Coins are subject to availability.

Rosland is a seller and purchaser of collectable coins and precious metals. Rosland is not a broker/dealer.

No broker/client or fiduciary relationship exists between Rosland and its customers, and Rosland does not warrant that the precious metals it sells are fit for any particular purpose. Rosland may, and usually does, make a profit on the precious metals it sells to its customers. Please be aware that precious metals and coins may appreciate, depreciate, or stay the same depending on a variety of factors – past changes in value are no indication of future changes in value. The decision to purchase or sell coins and precious metals, and which coins and precious metals to purchase or sell, is the customer's decision alone, and purchases and sales should be made subject to the customer's own research, prudence and judgment. Whilst every reasonable effort has been made to ensure that the information contained in this book is true and accurate at the date of publication, the statements made in this book merely reflect honestly held opinions. Rosland cannot guarantee that the information provided is 100% accurate and error free, and we provide no warranty as to the accuracy of the statements and information in this book. Rosland does not provide tax, investment, or legal advice or advisory services, and no one associated with Rosland is authorised to provide any such advice or services. Precious metals and coins are not specified investments under the Financial Services and Markets Act 2000 ('FSMA') and Rosland is not authorised under the FSMA by the Financial Conduct Authority. Consequently, customers will have no access to the Financial Ombudsman Service in the event of any dispute with Rosland and will not be able to bring a claim to the Financial Services Compensation Scheme should they suffer loss.

For more information, and to read the full terms and conditions in our Customer Agreement, please visit www.rosland.co.uk

CALL ROSLAND ON 0800 902 0000